STAR WARS®
DARTH MAUL™

STAR WARS
DARTH MAUL ™

SCRIPT
RON MARZ

PENCILS
JAN DUURSEMA

INKS
RICK MAGYAR

LETTERS
STEVE DUTRO

COLORS
DAVE McCAIG

COVER ARTIST
DREW STRUZAN

TITAN BOOKS

This book collects issues 1 through 4 of the comic-book series Star Wars®: Darth Maul™.

Titan Books, A Division of Titan Publishing Group Ltd.,
144 Southwark Street
London
SE1 0UP

www.titanbooks.com

First edition: June 2001
ISBN: 1-84023-285-4

10 9 8 7 6 5 4 3 2

Printed in Italy

BLACK SUN IS ORGANIZED UNDER **ONE** MASTER.

BENEATH HIM ARE NINE LIEUTENANTS...

...NINE **VIGOS**...

...WHO CURRY FAVOR WITH THE MASTER AND VIE FOR POWER.

EACH VIGO IS RESPONSIBLE FOR AN ENTIRE SYSTEM, EACH WITH THEIR OWN ARMY OF ENFORCERS AND BASE OF OPERATIONS.

MAKE NO MISTAKE...THE OPPONENT YOU FACE IS **FORMIDABLE.**

BUT ANY BEAST, NO MATTER HOW LARGE, IS HELPLESS ONCE ITS HEAD HAS BEEN SEVERED.

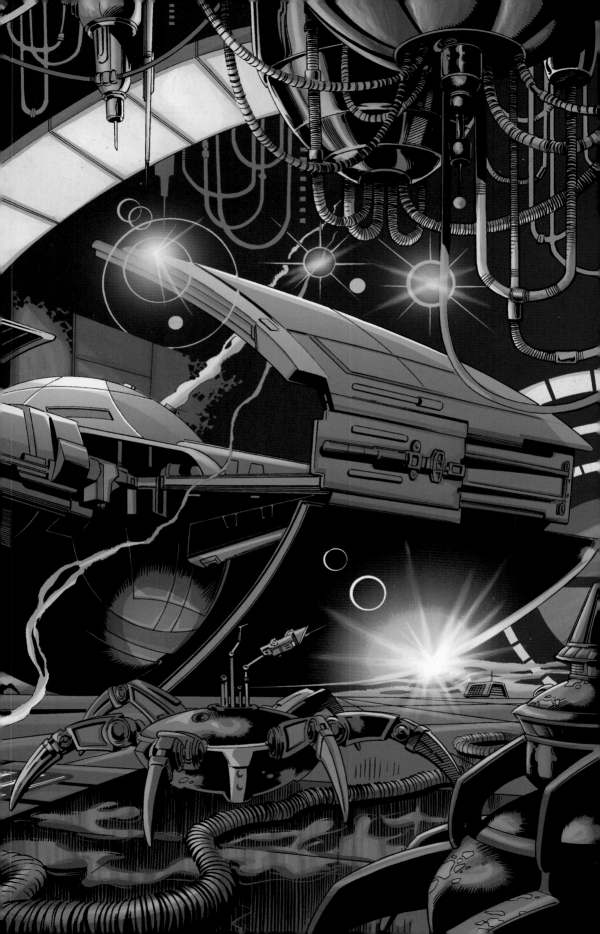

...please...

...you...

...YOU CAN'T DO THIS!

...PLEASE!

KZZT

VROOSH

CH-CHAK

gakk

GAK

CLOSE IT.

MASTER?

WHAT ARE YOU *DOING*, MASTER LEX?

PLEASE, I'VE *SEEN* WHAT HE DOES! DON'T LEAVE US TO HIM!

BLACK SUN SURVIVES AS LONG AS I SURVIVE. BUT YOU AND THE VIGOS, ASA...

...YOU AND THE VIGOS ARE EXPENDABLE. YOUR DEATHS WILL BUY ME THE TIME I NEED TO ESCAPE.

CURSE YOU! I CAME HERE TO WARN YOU AND *THIS* IS HOW YOU REPAY ME?!

LOYALTY IS OFTEN ITS *OWN* REWARD.

GOODBYE, ASA.

EEYAH!

...NO...

STAR WARS®
DARTH MAUL™
SKETCH GALLERY

FEATURING CHARACTER STUDIES BY ARTIST
JAN DUURSEMA